Grade 7

The Syllabus of Examinations should be read for details of requirements, especially those for scales, aural tests and sight-reading. Attention should be paid to the Special Notices on the front inside cover, where warning is given of changes.

The syllabus is obtainable from music dealers or from The Associated Board of the Royal Schools of Music, 14 Bedford Square, London WC1B 3JG (please send stamped addressed envelope measuring about 9×6 ins.).

In overseas centres, information may be obtained from the Local Representative or Resident Secretary.

Requirements

SCALES AND ARPEGGIOS (from memory)

Scales legato or staccato, as directed by the examiner:
(i) in similar motion, hands together one octave apart, and each hand separately, in the keys specified in one of the following groups chosen by the candidate (minors in melodic *and* harmonic forms) (four octaves):
Group 1: C, D, E, F♯, B♭, A♭ majors and minors
Group 2: G, A, B, F, E♭, D♭ majors and minors
(ii) in similar motion, hands together a third apart, in the major and harmonic minor keys of the group chosen for (i) (four octaves)
(iii) in contrary motion, both hands beginning and ending on the key-note (unison) in the major and harmonic minor keys chosen for (i) (two octaves)
(iv) legato *only*, in thirds, each hand separately, in the key of C major (two octaves)
(v) staccato *only*, in sixths, each hand separately (fingered 1 & 5), in the key of C major (two octaves)

Chromatic Scales legato or staccato, as directed:
(i) in similar motion, hands together one octave apart, and each hand separately, beginning on any note named by the examiner (four octaves)
(ii) in contrary motion, hands beginning and ending on the same note (unison), beginning on C and F♯ (two octaves)

Arpeggios legato *only*, in similar motion, hands together one octave apart, and each hand separately:
(i) the major and minor common chords, in first inversion only, of the keys of the scale group chosen above (four octaves)
(ii) dominant seventh chords, in root position only, in the keys of the scale group chosen above (three octaves)

PLAYING BY SIGHT (see current syllabus)

AURAL TESTS (see current syllabus)

THREE PIECES

Candidates should choose one piece from Group A, one piece from Group B, and the third piece *either* from Group C *or* from the further alternatives listed below:

Gounod La Pervenche
Heller Nuits blanches, Op.82 No.7
These are included in More Romantic Pieces for Piano, Book V, *published by the Associated Board*

Editor for the Associated Board: **Lionel Salter**

A:1
SONATA in B minor

Edited by
Howard Ferguson

SCARLATTI, Kp.197 (L.147)

Source: MS copy, Conservatorio di Musica Arrigo Boito, Parma. All dynamics and marks of articulation are editorial.

4

A:2
FUGA ALLA SARABANDA
No.3 from 'Four Concert Pieces for Piano'

BERNARD STEVENS

B:1
SONATA in E
First movement

Edited by
Howard Ferguson

HAYDN, Hob.XVI/31

Source: an early MS copy in the Wissenschaftliche Allgemeinbibliothek, Schwerin, headed *E♯ Sonata per il Clavi Cembalo Del Sig^re. Giuseppe Haydn.*
Dynamics, ornaments in brackets and a few slurs and articulation marks are editorial.

B:2
SONATA in E flat
Third movement

Edited by
Harold Craxton

BEETHOVEN, WoO 47/1

Dynamics in square brackets are editorial.

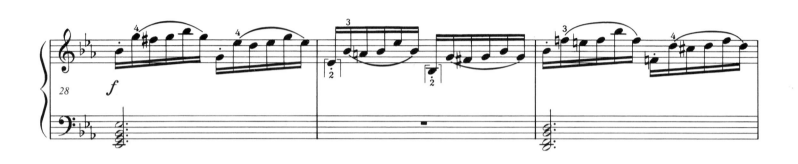

C:1
TOCCATA
No.1 from 'Five Pieces for Piano'

EDWIN CARR

C:2

CADIZ TANGO

DAVID GOW

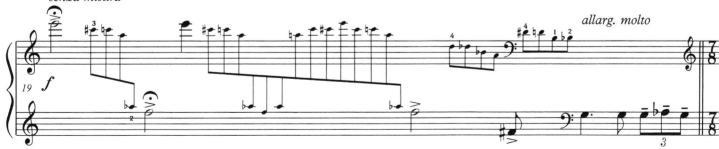

Tempo giusto